Humpty Dumpty Dumpty

by Thomas Moore
and Pam Schiller

Illustrated by
Mark Corcoran

SRA

A Division of The McGraw-Hill Companies

www.sra4kids.com

SRA/McGraw-Hill

A Division of The **McGraw·Hill** *Companies*

Send all inquiries to:
SRA/McGraw-Hill
8787 Orion Place
Columbus, OH 43240-4027

Printed in the United States of America.

ISBN 0-07-572408-1

4 5 6 7 8 9 QST 06 05 04 03

Humpty Dumpty sat on a wall.

Humpty Dumpty had a great fall.

All the king's horses and all the king's men
Couldn't put Humpty Dumpty together again.

But Mr. Moore knew just what to do.
He picked up the pieces and used his glue.

Now Humpty Dumpty's as good as new!
He wants to dance and so do you!

Everybody likes to Humpty Dumpty Dumpty.
Everybody likes to Humpty Dumpty Dumpty.

O-o-o-o-h, Humpty Dumpty sat on the wall.
Humpty Dumpty had a great fall.
Humpty Dumpty Dumpty.

All the boys like to Humpty Dumpty Dumpty.
All the boys like to Humpty Dumpty Dumpty.

O-o-o-o-h, Humpty Dumpty sat on the wall.
Humpty Dumpty had a great fall.
Humpty Dumpty Dumpty.

All the girls like to Humpty Dumpty Dumpty.
All the girls like to Humpty Dumpty Dumpty.

O-o-o-o-h, Humpty Dumpty sat on the wall.
Humpty Dumpty had a great fall.
Humpty Dumpty Dumpty.

Everybody likes to Humpty Dumpty Dumpty.
Everybody likes to Humpty Dumpty Dumpty.

O-o-o-o-h, Humpty Dumpty sat on the wall.
Humpty Dumpty had a great fall.
Humpty Dumpty Dumpty.

Now Humpty Dumpty's better than new.
Humpty Dumpty Dumpty.